MEGATRON

SUPER OPTIMUS PRIME

STRONGARM

TRANSFORMERS ENERGON

CONTENTS

TRANSFORMERS ENERGON

Pedigree®

Published by Pedigree Books Limited
Beech Hill House, Walnut Gardens, Exeter, Devon, EX4 4DH.
E-mail books@pedigreegroup.co.uk
Published 2004

Licensing by Hasbro Properties Group

Original material created by Dreamwave Productions.

£6.99

AUTOBOTS

OPTIMUS PRIME is the powerful and courageous leader of the AUTOBOTS. Along with his increadable strength, he possesses great wisdom and believes that freedom is the right of all sentient beings. He has vowed to fight against the evil DECEPTICONS in their quest to plunder Earth of its vast Energon resources. Always in favour of peace, OPTIMUS PRIME will not hesitate to use his great powers and vast arsenal of weopons to stop MEGATRON and the DECEPTICONS from threatening the universe.

HOT SHOT, once a stubborn and headstrong young fighter, is now a seasonal AUTOBOT warrior. After fighting bravely in the UNICRON battles, he has proven to be a skilled soldier with leadership potential. HOT SHOT is one of the fastest AUTOBOTS, capable of great speed in both robot and vehicle modes. He is able to POWERLINX with his good friend, INFERNO, and is a force to be reconed with during the battle for Energon.

INFERNO is a true AUTOBOT, always looking out for the safety and well being of those around him. In vehicle mode, he is a powerful firetruck capable of heroric, and often dangerous, search and rescue missions. In robot mode, he is a skilled targetmaster and sniper. INFERNO thinks before he acts, aware of the consequences of his actions. He is able to POWERLINX with HOT SHOT and always provides a well thought-out approach before battle.

STRONGARM ia an AUTOBOT OMNICON who would rather work than fight. He is able to manafacture raw Energon into Energon Chips and useful tools and weopons, a valuable energy source to the AUTOBOTS. He can often be found alongide his OMNICON brothers gathering precious Energon deposits. Although STRONGARM chooses not to fight, his contributions to the AUTOBOTS will play a major role during the battle for Energon.

DECEPTICONS

MEGATRON has been reborn. Totally reformatted by UNICRON, he now possesses an intense arsenal of weopons that will make him an unstoppable force during the battle for ENERGON. In robot mode, MEGATRON fights hi enemies with a remote triple-change tank module. In Gunship mode, he can use his hyper-power wings and rotating cannons to rain terror from above. The look of MEGATRON ha changed, but his goal of universal conquest remains the same.

SCORPONOK is a power-hungry warrior who believes that he is the rightful leader of the DECEPTICONS. He can back up this claim with a three-mode arsenal and a nasty attitude. In scorpion mode, beware of his huge mechanical claws and energon stinger. In vehicle mode, SCORPONOK is a powerful jet construction with a talent for destruction.

STARSCREAM has been reborn and is still caught in his own personal battle of choosing the side of goos or evil. The high dose of ENERGON, which bought him back to life, has also given him incredible powers that he is learning to control. Starream's new hyper power turns him into pure energy, allowing him to ghost from one location to the next. Thiss phantom ability, combined with his new power sword, makes him a dangerous adversary to all that oppose him, including MEGATRON.

autobots
TRANSFORMERS
ENERGON
POSTER 1

TRANSFORMERS
ENERGON
POSTER 2

TRANSFORMERS ENERGON™

WHAT LIES BENEATH

part 1

EARTH:
WESTERN AUSTRALIA_
AND TO THINK...

EXPLORATORY EXCAVATION/
DRILLING OPERATION_
RENERGY PROJECT

BURN IT ALL DOWN, SHOW THEM...THE UTTER CONTEMPT THEY SO RICHLY DESERVE!
...I USED TO CALL THIS THE DULLEST PLACE ON PLANET EARTH!

HUMANS--YOU HAVE OUR SINCERE GRATITUDE FOR UNCOVERING SUCH A RICH VEIN OF ENERGON...
...BUT YOUR PRESENCE--LOCALLY AND GLOBALLY--IS NO LONGER REQUIRED.
THWUM!

WE CLAIM THIS REGION, THIS PLANET AND ALL ITS RESOURCES IN THE NAME OF THE TERRORCONS...

SPOW!!
...AND UNICRON!

...ATTACKED WITHOUT WARNING, APPEARING--WITNESSES CLAIM--OUT OF NOWHERE. THE GOVERNMENT AND MILITARY ARE IN CRISIS TALKS...
...ALTERENERGY'S SPECIAL CONSULTANT, DR. BRIAN JONES COULD NOT BE REACHED FOR COMMENT...
...A LARGE DEPOSIT OF O1 SOURCE, WHICH ANALYSTS BELIEVE WILL SUPPLEMENT EARTH'S DWINDLING FOSSIL FUEL RESERVES...
...PROTESTORS, CONCERNED ABOUT THE LONG-TERM EFFECTS OF BLANKET STRIP MINING AND DRILLING HAD PLANNED A DEMONSTRATION...
RAD, DR. JONES? YOU GETTING THIS?

ALTERENERGY MOBILE COMMAND_
ALTERENERGY
IN DOOM-LADEN TECHNICOLOR, CARLOS...

...WITH GRISLY, DIGITAL SURROUNDSOUND.
WHAT ARE THEY? WHAT DO THEY WANT?
AND...WHERE'S MY SON?! WHERE'S CHAD?
WORKING ON IT, DR. JONES. HANG IN THERE...

CARLOS, ANYTHING?

COMSAT ALPHA_
IT'S A MESS DOWN THERE, RAD. I READ SEVERAL LIFESIGNS, BUT NO VISUAL I.D. ON CHAD... I MEAN, KICKER.
YOU THINKING WHAT I'M THINKING?

SUBJECT 01-RAPTOR TYPE-
SUBJECT 02-EAGLE TYPE-
SUBJECT 03 -PUMA TYPE-
SUBJECT 04 -SCORPION TYPE-
YEAH, I AM. SO FAR, THEY'VE STUCK TO ONE MODE, BUT I'M BETTING THEY'RE TRANSFORMERS.
IT'S STARTED AGAIN!
TRANSFORMERS?
YE-EH. TRANSFORMERS. IT'S A...WILD STORY. BEEN WHAT, CARLOS, TEN YEARS?
TEN YEARS, TWO MONTHS, THREE DAYS AND SOME ODD HOURS AND MINUTES. NOT THAT I'VE BEEN COUNTING...
WE WERE KIDS. AND, WELL, INSANE AS IT SOUNDS, WE STUMBLED INTO THIS BONA FIDE INTERGALACTIC CONFLICT.
14579FT
INCOMING FLYING OBJECTS
VREEEP!
TWO FACTIONS OF WARRING GIANT ROBOTS, AND ANOTHER RACE, SMALLER THAN THE OTHERS, CAUGHT IN THE MID--
CARLOS? WHAT HAVE WE GOT? TALK TO ME...
RAD
AUSTRALIAN AIR FORCE, RAD. MULTIPLE LAUNCHES FROM BONNIE ROCK AND SOUTHERN CROSS. F-19 VIPERS...

"...LOADED FOR BEAR!"

THIS IS *BEYOND* BAD! THEY WON'T KNOW WHAT'S *HIT* THEM!
BAD? BUT... THEY ATTACKED US. THEY DESERVE--
NOT THE *DECEPTICONS*, DOCTOR...*IF* THAT'S WHAT THEY ARE. NO, I MEAN THE MILITARY...
...THEY DON'T STAND A CHANCE!

VOOOOM!
WHAT'S THE *DEAL?*
GEEZ!

NOT AGAIN, PLEASE... NOT AGAIN.
KAFF! PFT! C'MON--LET'S GET OUT OF HERE!
I'M ALL FOR CAMPAIGNING ON BEHALF OF MOTHER EARTH, BUT ANOTHER TIME!

ALEXIS?
HEAVEN HELP US ALL...

HEY! HEY! YOU LOT...GO! GET OUT OF HERE!
WHAT? BUT...

...NO. WE'RE NOT GOING ANYWHERE!
ALEXIS!
THIS IS A LEGITIMATE PROTEST. THEY CAN'T--

GEEZ, LADY...JUST GO!
THIS GUY...I DON'T THINK HE CARES ABOUT THE ENVIRONMENT!
MY ADVICE TO ONE AND ALL IS...

...GET OVER IT!
VRAZ!
VRAZ!
VRAZ!

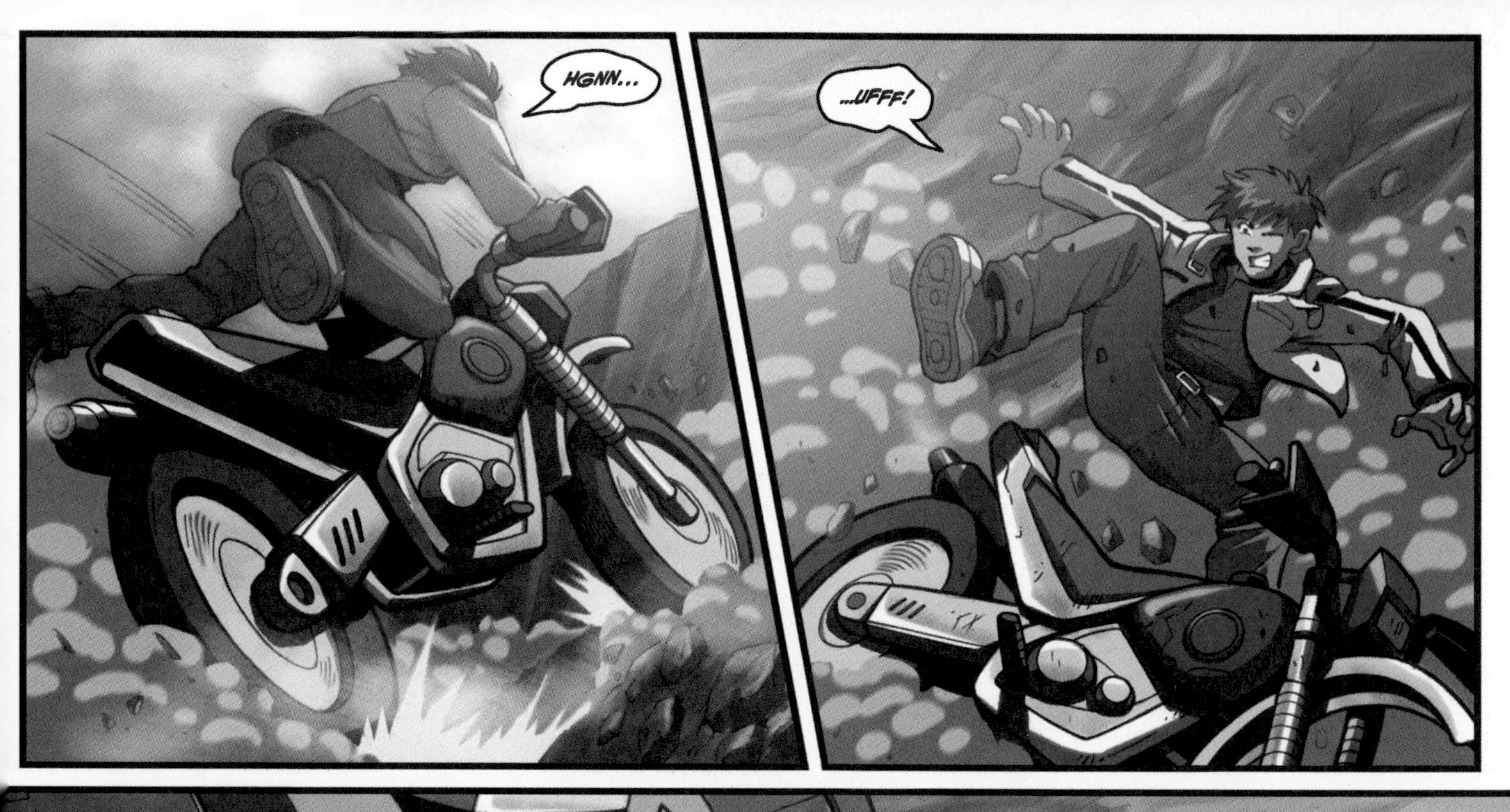
HGNN...
...UFFF!

GET UP... GET UP!
ALEXIS, C'MON! THAT...THING. IT... IT'LL EAT US UP AND SPIT US OUT.
ALEXIS!
DAMN...

WHH-WHAT...ARE YOU DOING? GET OUT OF HERE...WHILE YOU CAN...
YEAH, UH-HUH. STRANGELY...
RRRAH-AH-HA-HA!
...THAT'S A TRICK I NEVER REALLY LEARNED THE FIRST TIME AROUND!

ALTERENERGY MOBILE COMMAND, HANGAR SIX_
CAN YOU FIND HIM?
RAD?
SURE, SURE. TRUST ME. OLDER I MAY BE...

...BUT THANKFULLY I'M NO WISER.
I'LL FIND YOUR SON, DR. JONES. I KNOW HOW MUCH HE MEANS TO YOU.

TO ME... YES. AND TO ALTERENERGY. IT'S...
I CAN'T EXPLAIN. BUT YOU HAVE TO BRING HIM BACK, ALIVE. OUR FUTURE, AS A RACE, DEPENDS ON HIM. HE'S... SPECIAL.
YEAH? AND I THOUGHT HE WAS A SIXTEEN YEAR-OLD PUNK WITH A NEED FOR SPEED.

JUST GOES TO SHOW, YOU THINK YOU KNOW SOMEONE...

...AND THERE'S MORE TO THEM THAN MEETS THE EYE.
HANG TIGHT, DR. JONES...

...I'LL BE BACK BEFORE YOU CAN SAY 'WORLD DOMINATION'!

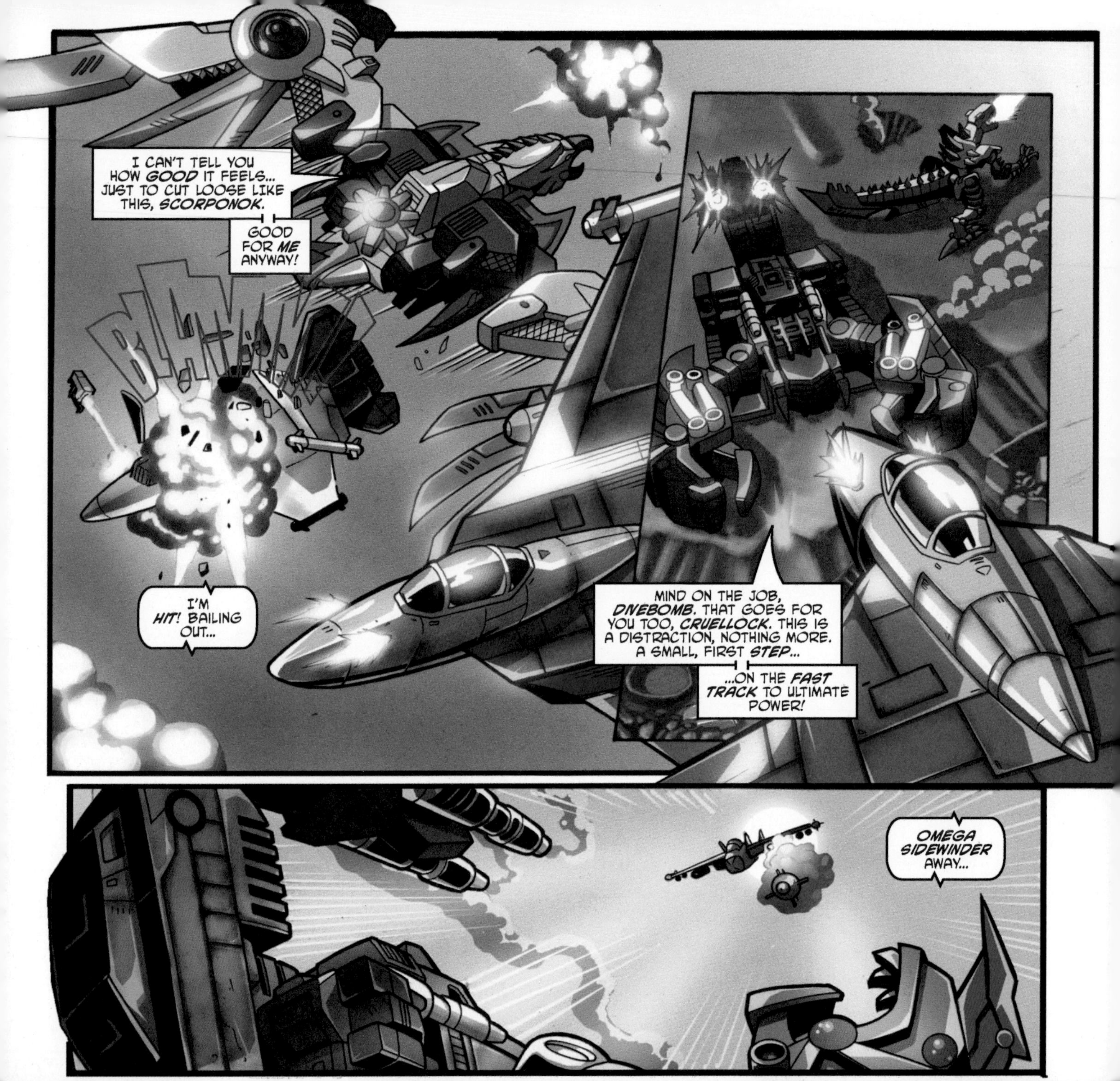
I CAN'T TELL YOU HOW GOOD IT FEELS... JUST TO CUT LOOSE LIKE THIS, SCORPONOK.
GOOD FOR ME ANYWAY!
BLAM
I'M HIT! BAILING OUT...
MIND ON THE JOB, DIVEBOMB. THAT GOES FOR YOU TOO, CRUELLOCK. THIS IS A DISTRACTION, NOTHING MORE. A SMALL, FIRST STEP...
...ON THE FAST TRACK TO ULTIMATE POWER!
OMEGA SIDEWINDER AWAY...

WHAKOOOM

DIRECT HIT ON TARGET. ATTEMPTING TO CONFIRM KILL...
KRRRKT!
THE KILLING...

...STARTS NOW!
HEY, HEY! LEAVE SOME FOR US!
TIDAL WAVE, INSECTICON--GOOD. READY THE ENERGON SIPHONS...

HOLY--
IT'S A ROUT! CARLOS, GIVE ME SOME GOOD NEWS...
THINK I'VE GOT HIM. OR THEM. BUT...
BUT? CARLOS!
"...YOU'RE NOT GOING TO GET TO THEM IN TIME!"
THIS IS IT.
LOOK AWAY.
EH? NO WAY. I--
LOOK AWAY!

FWASSH!
EEARG!
WHAT WAS THAT?
THE PLAN WAS TO WAIT UNTIL DARK AND THEN BREAK IN, LIGHT UP THE DIG SITE AND OUR PROTEST BANNER FOR THE TV NEWS CAMERAS...
...BUT HEY, WORKS FOR BIG, BAD BEAST 'BOTS TOO!
GET ON!
BUT--
GET ON! BASED ON WHAT I SAW OF YOUR DRIVING. THE ODDS FAVOR THE FEMALE TOUCH.
WHAT'S YOUR NAME, KID?
KICKER.
KICKER? OHH-KAY. I'M ALEXIS. NOW HANG ON...

"...WE'RE NOT OUT OF THIS *YET!*"
RELAY THE NEW INTERCEPT VECTOR. WHAT ABOUT OUR, AH, *HOTLINE?*
RAD, THE SIGNALS ARE *MOBILE*. I DON'T KNOW HOW, BUT THEY ARE.
SLIPSTREAM PULSE SENT...

"...LET'S HOPE SOMEONE'S *HOME* TO PICK UP."
CYBERTRON_
THE COUNCIL UNDERSTANDS YOUR CONCERNS, *OPTIMUS PRIME*...

THE HIGH HALLS_
...BUT WITHOUT SOME MORE *COMPELLING* EVIDENCE OF *UNICRON'S* SURVIVAL AND THIS SUPPOSED *THREAT* TO EARTH WE CANNOT ACT.
BUT, *LEVITACUS*, MEGATRON--
--IS *DEAD*.

FOUR OF YOUR OWN TROOPERS SAW TO IT PERSONALLY. WE HAVE THEIR TESTIMONY FROM THE UNICRON BATTLES.
BY YOUR OWN ADMISSION, YOU DOUBT THE CREDULITY OF MEGATRON'S SURVIVAL... EVEN AS A DISEMBODIED SPARK!

...
PERHAPS. BUT I TELL YOU I WAS THERE...ON THE SURFACE OF UNICRON. I SAW SCORPONOK--AND OTHER DECEPTICONS--LEAVE FOR EARTH...

YE-ES. ACCORDING TO YOUR REPORT, YOU ACCESSED SOME VAST, SENTIENT INTELLIGENCE AT THE HEART OF CYBERTRON.
AND THIS... SIG-OMEGA...IT GRANTED YOU A... VISION?

YOU'LL FORGIVE A DEGREE OF SCEPTICISM, OPTIMUS PRIME, BUT WE ARE THE HIGH COUNCIL...THE ANCIENTS, THE FOUNDERS...
...AND WE HAVE NEVER HEARD OF SUCH AN ENTITY.
STILL, IT MAY BE UNWISE TO SUCCUMB TO THE COMPLACENCY THAT HAS PLAGUED US IN THE PAST...

CAN YOU HEAR ANYTHING?
SHH.
A FEW WORDS. THERE'S--

HANG ON! I THINK...

THWAMM!
...HE'S COMING!
AND HOW!

I'M GOING--
--ALONE.

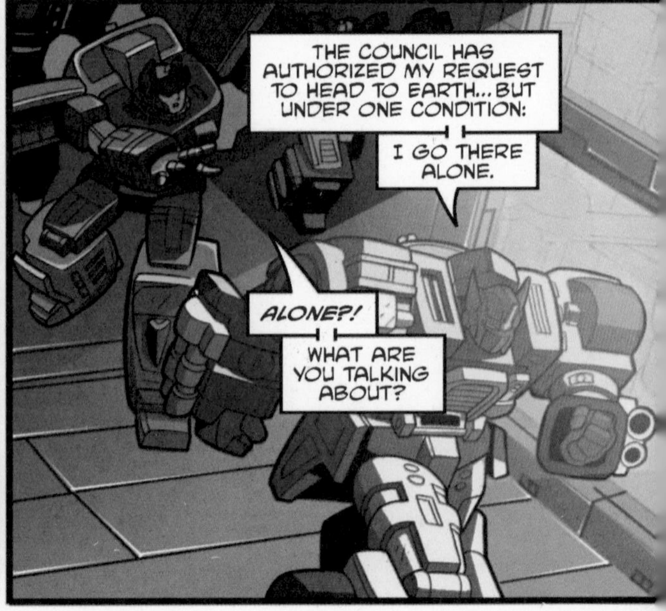
THE COUNCIL HAS AUTHORIZED MY REQUEST TO HEAD TO EARTH...BUT UNDER ONE CONDITION:
I GO THERE ALONE.
ALONE?!
WHAT ARE YOU TALKING ABOUT?

THERE'S NO OTHER CHOICE. CURRENTLY, CYBERTRON CANNOT SPARE THE PERSONNEL NECESSARY FOR A FULL-SCALE ENGAGEMENT.
NONETHELESS, WE CAN'T TURN OUR BACKS ON THE EARTH. NOT WITH SCORP-

PRIME...
WE'RE COMING WITH YOU, *ALL* OF US.
YOU THINK WE'RE GOING TO MISS AN OPPORTUNITY TO STRUT OUR SERVOS--
THANK YOU. *ALL* OF YOU... BUT--

CYBERTRONIANS...
HNN! WHAT--?

...THE END OF DAYS IS UPON YOU!
TO BE CONTINUED.

TRANSFORMERS ENERGON

POSTER 3

Super Optimus Prime

TRANSFORMERS
ENERGON
POSTER 4

TRANSFORMERS ENERGON™
WHAT LIES BENEATH
part 2
GUIDO

CYBERTRON: THE HALLS OF JUSTICE_

PRIME-- WHO *ARE* THEY?

I KNOW WHO THEY *WERE*, *HOT SHOT*. THE REAL QUESTION IS...

ZOW!!

"...WHO AND WHAT ARE THEY NOW?"

ONCE, PERHAPS.
ALONG WITH AIRAZOR, CHEETOR AND THE DECEPTICON, TERRORSAUR. THE WERE LOST IN THE UNICRON BATTLES, PRESUMED DEAD I REALIZE NOW...

CRY HAVOC--
--AND LET SLIP THE BEASTS OF THE APOCALYPSE!
UH?
LOOK CLOSELY...
I...OHH...NO. NO! IS THAT... RHINOX?

"...HOW HOPELESSLY OPTIMISTIC THAT WAS."

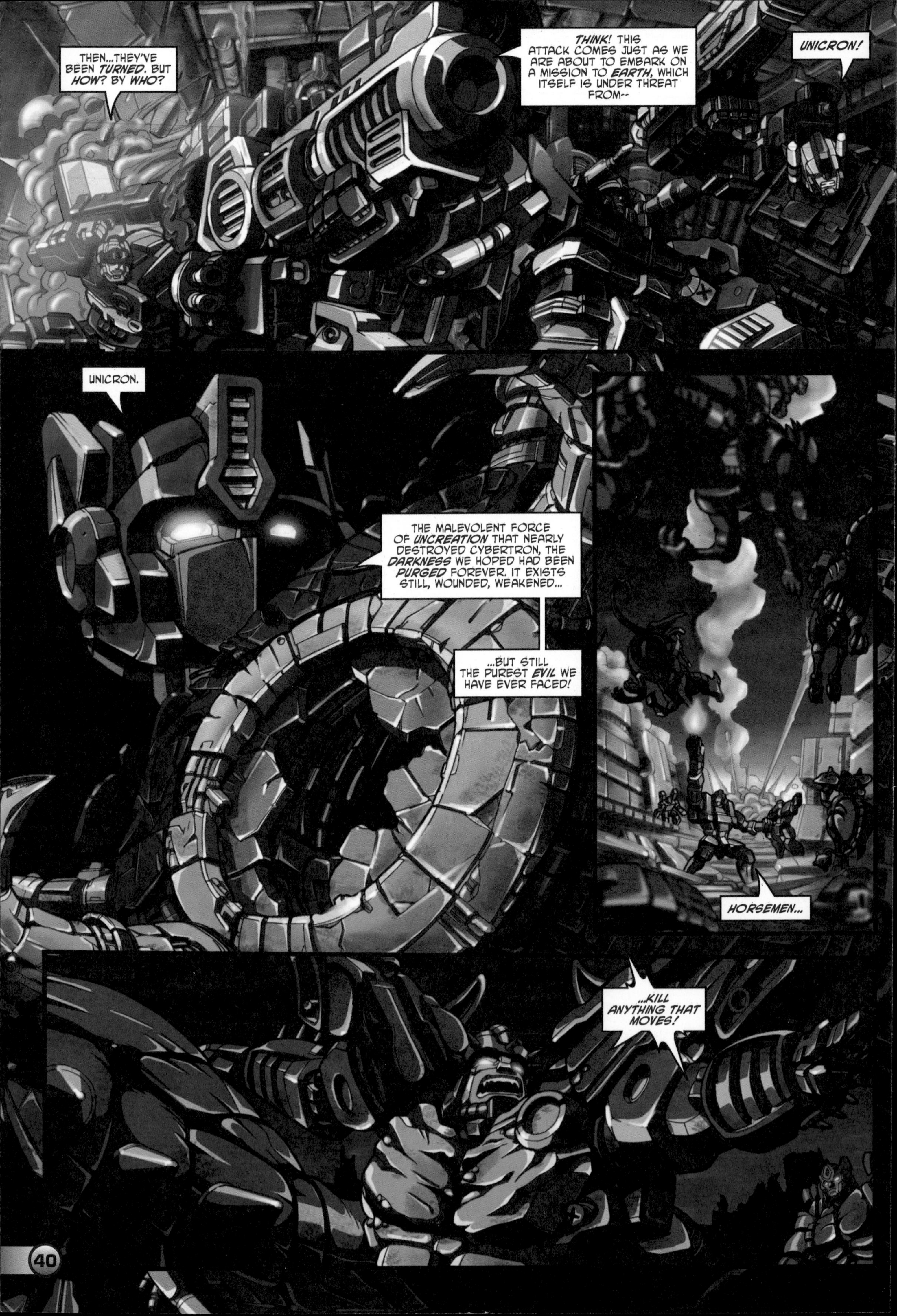
THEN...THEY'VE BEEN *TURNED*. BUT *HOW*? BY *WHO*?
THINK! THIS ATTACK COMES JUST AS WE ARE ABOUT TO EMBARK ON A MISSION TO *EARTH*, WHICH ITSELF IS UNDER THREAT FROM--
UNICRON!
UNICRON.
THE MALEVOLENT FORCE OF *UNCREATION* THAT NEARLY DESTROYED CYBERTRON, THE *DARKNESS* WE HOPED HAD BEEN *PURGED* FOREVER. IT EXISTS STILL, WOUNDED, WEAKENED...
...BUT STILL THE PUREST *EVIL* WE HAVE EVER FACED!
HORSEMEN...
...KILL ANYTHING THAT MOVES!

WAR:
DEATH:
FAMINE:
PESTILENCE:
IT'S BEEN WHAT... MOMENTS? AND ALREADY... SO MANY DEAD!
BACK-UP'S ON ITS WAY, BUT TO BE BRUTALLY HONEST...
...IT MAY BE TOO LITTLE TOO LATE!

WHILE WE FUNCTION, NFERNO...

...THERE'S ALWAYS HOPE!
NO.

KRUNNK!
HOPE IS GONE.
OPTIMUS PRIME!

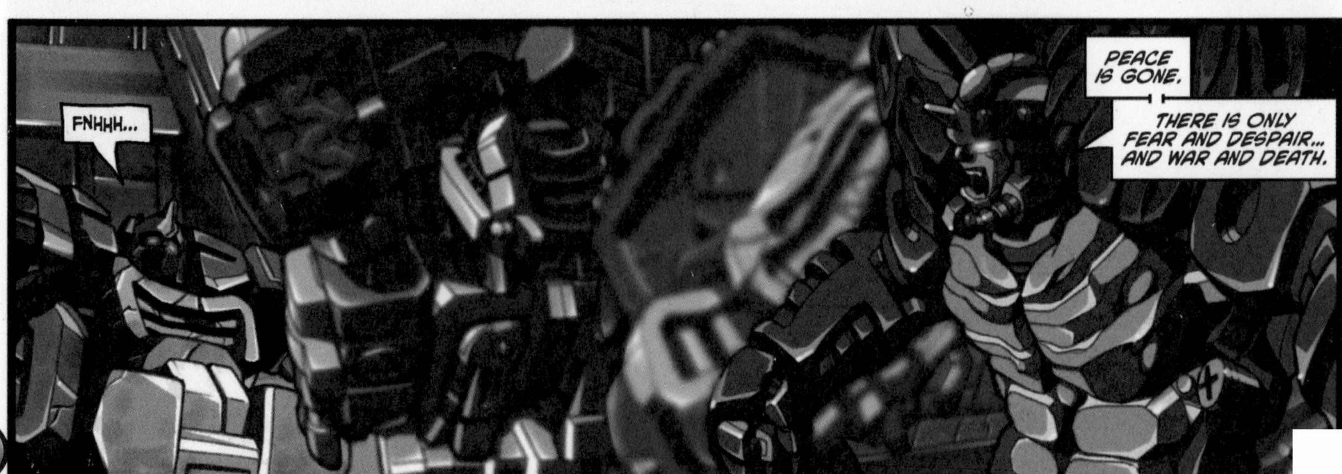
PEACE IS GONE.
THERE IS ONLY FEAR AND DESPAIR... AND WAR AND DEATH.
FNHHH...

WE ARE HARBINGERS OF THE DARKNESS THAT WILL CONSUME YOU ALL, THE FIRE AND FURY OF CHAOS UNBOUND.
HIS WILL IS OURS, AND THIS FUTILE BID TO THWART HIS NINTH EMERGENCE...
...MUST DIE WITH YOU.
FROKK!
GNNF!
YOU ARE A PRIME, AND YET YOUR POWER IS LITTLE MORE THAN THAT OF A FOOT SOLDIER. YOU WILL NEVER KNOW...
...HOW MUCH MORE YOU COULD HAVE BEEN!
VOOM!
VOOM!
EH? OH...
YOU WILL ALL DIE SCREAMING, IN IGNORANCE, BLIND TO WHAT LIES BENEATH. THUS FALLS CYBERTRON...

"...AND WITH IT EARTH."
WESTERN AUSTRALIA_
ALTERENERGY EXPLORATORY EXCAVATION/DRILLING SITE_

DIVEBOMB, WHAT IS THE DELAY? THE HUMANS' BID TO DEFEND THEIR WORLD WAS AN AMUSING DISTRACTION...
...BUT I AM NOW IMPATIENT TO BEGIN.
EACH ENERGON ACCUMULATOR HAS TO BE PROPERLY PREPPED, SCORPONOK. ONCE THE SOURCE IS TAPPED, THE FLOW RATE HAS TO BE CONSTANT. IF IT FLUCTUATES EVEN SLIGHTLY, THEN...
WELL?

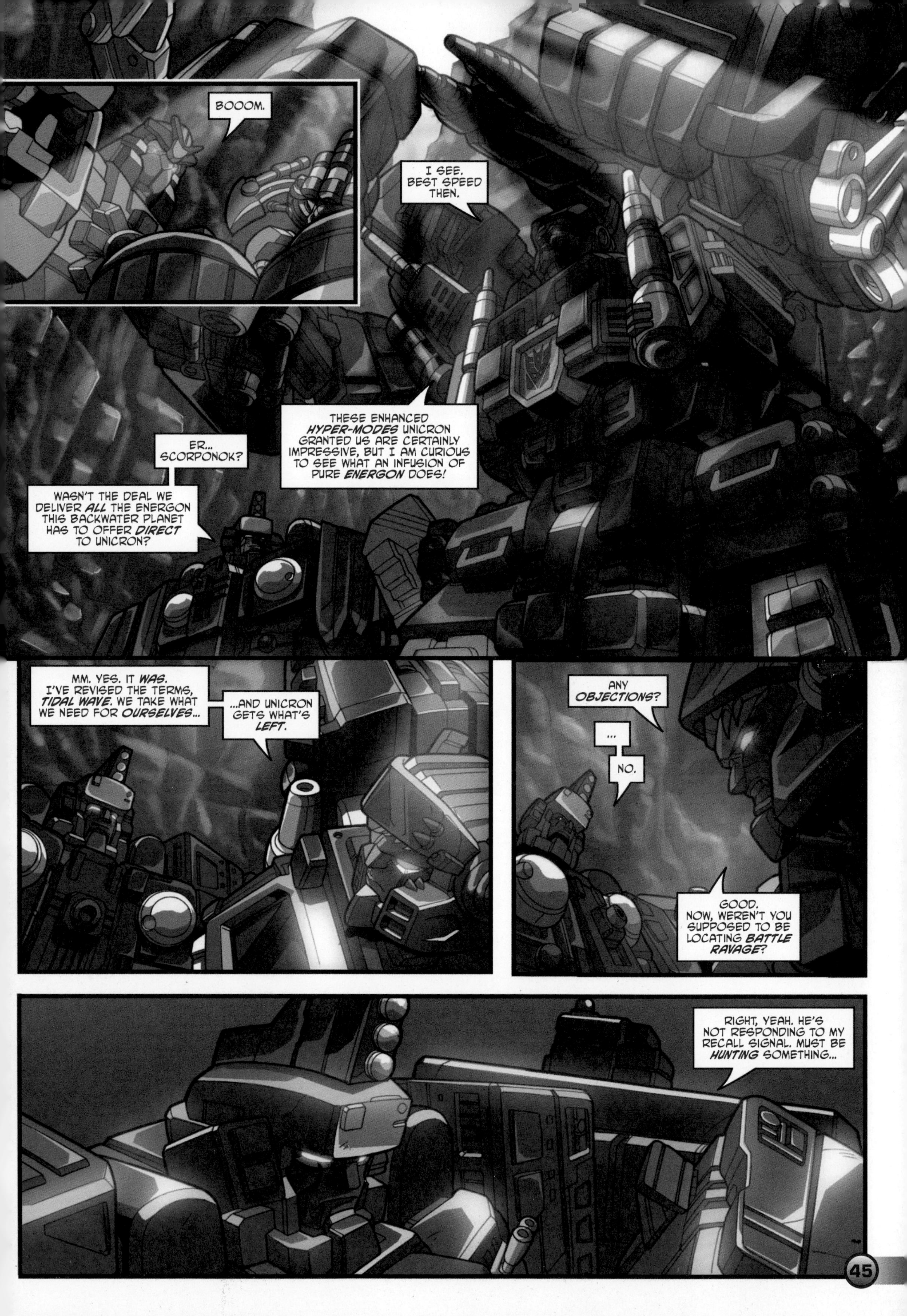
BOOOM.
I SEE. BEST SPEED THEN.
THESE ENHANCED HYPER-MODES UNICRON GRANTED US ARE CERTAINLY IMPRESSIVE, BUT I AM CURIOUS TO SEE WHAT AN INFUSION OF PURE ENERGON DOES!
ER... SCORPONOK?
WASN'T THE DEAL WE DELIVER ALL THE ENERGON THIS BACKWATER PLANET HAS TO OFFER DIRECT TO UNICRON?
MM. YES. IT WAS. I'VE REVISED THE TERMS, TIDAL WAVE. WE TAKE WHAT WE NEED FOR OURSELVES...
...AND UNICRON GETS WHAT'S LEFT.
ANY OBJECTIONS?
...
NO.
GOOD. NOW, WEREN'T YOU SUPPOSED TO BE LOCATING BATTLE RAVAGE?
RIGHT, YEAH. HE'S NOT RESPONDING TO MY RECALL SIGNAL. MUST BE HUNTING SOMETHING...

"...YOU KNOW HOW HE GETS!"
THIRTY-MILES DUE SOUTH:
RR?
SNFF!
FRPH
HNGR!
FACE IT, ALEXIS... THIS GUY AIN'T GONNA TO GIVE UP!
EVER!
VRRM! VRM!
TELL ME, KICKER... DO YOU ALWAYS HAVE TO BE RIGHT?
UFF! ALWAYS.

NOT THAT I DON'T APPRECIATE THE SAVE, BUT ALL YOU'VE DONE IS GIVEN HIM A FEW MORE BONES TO SHARPEN HIS TEETH ON...
WE'LL SEE.
I TOLD YOU, STRANGE AS IT SOUNDS... THIS ISN'T MY FIRST RUN-IN WITH THESE CREATURES.
IT'S JUST A MATTER OF STAYING ONE STEP AHEAD OF--
GSSTKK!
HN--
--UUUUH!
RR-AHRAHGH!

CYBERTRON_
ONE BY ONE, OPTIMUS PRIME...

...THEY SUCCUMB.
THIS--
--IS HOW IT ENDS.

DARKNESS FALLS...
NUH--NO! IT CAAAN'T--

HNNK!
VAAP!
'VRZ' YOU LOT...

...SO NEED TO LIGHTEN UP!
'VRZ' OMNICONS-- HURT THEM!

'FRZ' YOUR WISH, SKYBLAST...
VOM!
...IS MY COMMAND!
AWRRK!

'CRZ' I LIKE THAT ABOUT YOU, ARCEE...SUCH DEDICATION TO DUTY. ME...
...I JUST LIKE TO SLICE 'N' DICE!
WAR! THEY WIELD PURE ENERGON, BEND IT TO THEIR WILL! THE--
ZAK!
'CRZ' BLABBERMOUTH!
'ZRZ' OPTIMUS PRIME? OVER-RUN SENDS HIS COMPLIMENTS. ASKED US TO LEND A HAND.
'ZRZ' HE SAYS TO 'GET IN TOUCH'. CYBERTRON HAS SOMETHING FOR YOU.
WHH...WHAT? I DON'T--

'ZRZ' OH...BUT YOU *DO!* YOU DID IT BEFORE.
BUT...THAT WAS AT A PRE-ARRANGED SITE. AN *UPLINK PLATFORM* IN THE SOUTHERN POLAR DISTRICT. THERE'S NO *TIME*, I CAN'T--

'ZRZ' OH...BUT YOU *CAN!* THE UPLINK PLATFORM WAS JUST A DEVICE, A DISTRACTION... TO GET YOU TO *OPEN* YOUR MIND. YOU'RE THE PRIME. *ANYWHERE* WILL DO.

ANYWHERE?
ANYWHERE.

INTEGRATION STABLE. WELCOME, OPTIMUS PRIME, TO THE *HUB*.
PLANETARY STABILITY IS UNDER *EXTREME* THREAT. READY FOR SYSTEM-WIDE *UPGRADE*...
BUT'--

PREPARE TO RECEIVE THE SPARK OF COMBINATION...
HH!

THE FATE OF MANY WORLDS DEPENDS ON YOU, OPTIMUS PRIME...

...DO NOT FALTER!
I WILL NOT. AT LAST...I UNDERSTAND.
OPTIMUS 1, OPTIMUS 2, OPTIMUS 3, OPTIMUS 4...
...POWERLINX!

'VRZ' NASTY!
YOU TOOK US BY SURPRISE, I GRANT YOU. WE DID NOT KNOW YOU HAD EVOLVED TO THIS STAGE.
BUT IN THE END YOUR LIMITED MASTERY OF ENERGON IS JUST NOT ENOUGH.
CHAK!
HHN!
WRONG.
WUNNCH!
IT'S ENOUGH.
THE OMNICONS GAVE ME THE TIME I NEEDED TO SEE THE MAJESTY THAT IS CYBERTRON...AND MY PLACE IN IT!

HOT SHOT. IT'S *TIME*...
RIGHT.

...FOR *TEAMWORK*!
ARRK?

GUESS IT'S YOU AND ME, *IRONHIDE*. A *WISE* HEAD...

...ON *YOUNG* SHOULDERS!

AUTOBOTS, OMNICONS...TAKE THEM DOWN!
MAXIMUM FORCE!

HORSEMEN!
WE ARE RECALLED. MOUNT YOUR STEEDS...

THIS IS BUT AN OPENING SKIRMISH, PRIME. NEXT TIME...

...WE WILL BE READY.
AS WILL WE.

WELL, IF THIS IS A VICTORY...I'D *HATE* TO SEE A DEFEAT.
BUT AT LEAST IT'S OVER.
NO, IT'S *NOT*.

THIS WAS MEANT TO *DELAY* US. HOT SHOT. WE *HAVE* TO GET TO A SPACE BRIDGE PORTAL--*NOW*!
WE HAVE ONE READY AND WAITING, OPTIMUS PRIME.
LEVITACUS...
IN WAYS THAT EVEN *WE* DO NOT FULLY UNDERSTAND, CYBERTRON HAS SPOKEN: THE CHAOS-BRINGER HAS *DECLARED WAR*...

"...AND *EARTH* IS THE BATTLEFIELD!
SCORPONOK--
--HE'S *BACK*.

WHERE HAVE YOU *BEEN*, BATTLE RAVAGE, AND...

...WHAT *EXACTLY* HAVE YOU BROUGHT ME?

OHHH.
I SEE. YES.
THIS RATHER ORDINARY SPECIMEN...

...MAY JUST BE THE KEY TO ULTIMATE POWER!
BIO SIGNATURE
JW001110001110
JC110001101001
JR100111000110
BIO SIGNATURE
HC101110001110
PC111000111000
BY000111000011
TO BE CONTINUED.

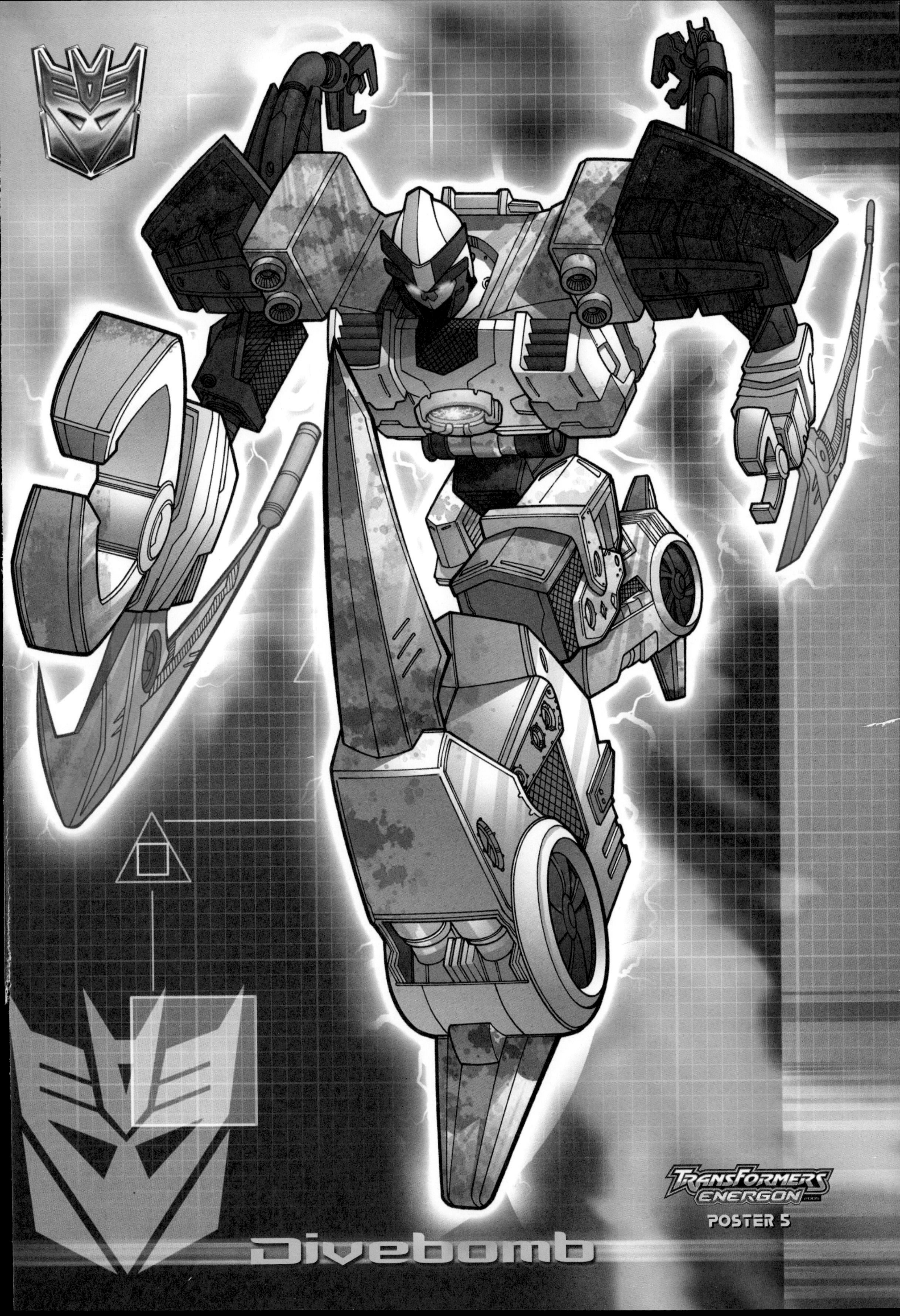
TRANSFORMERS ENERGON
POSTER 5
Divebomb

TRANSFORMERS
ENERGON
POSTER 6
Inferno

TRANSFORMERS ENERGON
POSTER 7
Scorponok